Jazz
Standards

VOLONTÈ&CO

FABER *ff* MUSIC

Anything Goes

Words and Music by Cole Porter

Bright swing

In old-en days a glimpse of stock-ing was looked on as some-thing shock-

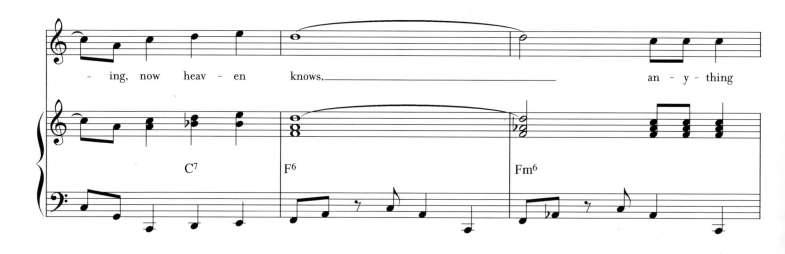

-ing, now heav-en knows,_____ an-y-thing

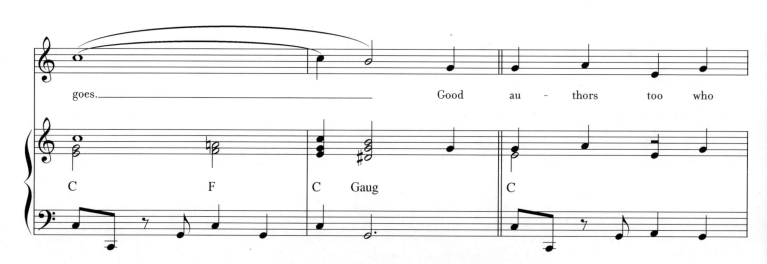

goes._____ Good au-thors too who

A Fine Romance

Words by Dorothy Fields

Music by Jerome Kern

A Foggy Day In London Town

Music and Lyrics by George Gershwin and Ira Gershwin

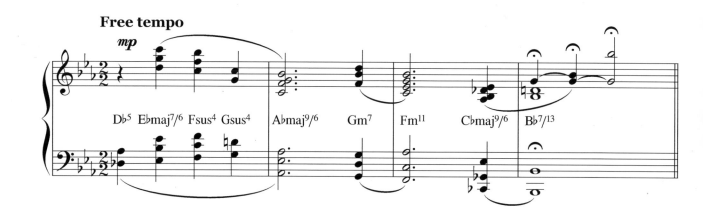

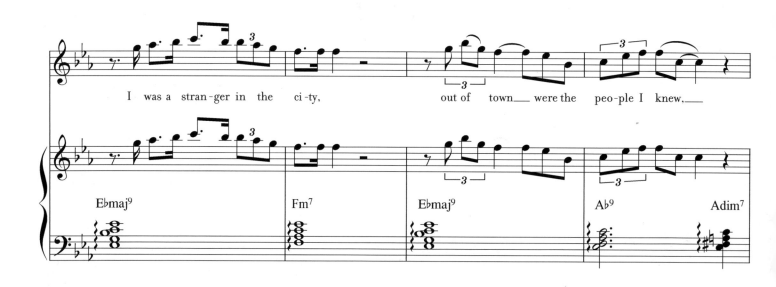

April In Paris

Words by E. Y. Harburg

Music by Vernon Duke

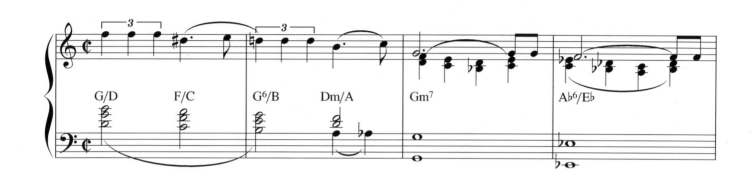

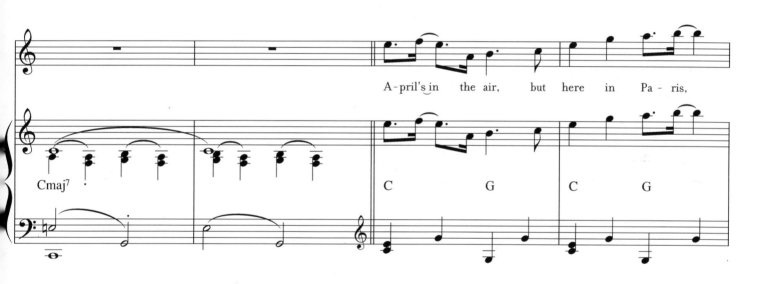

A-pril's in the air, but here in Pa-ris,

A-pril wears a dif-fe-rent gown. You can see her waltz-ing down the

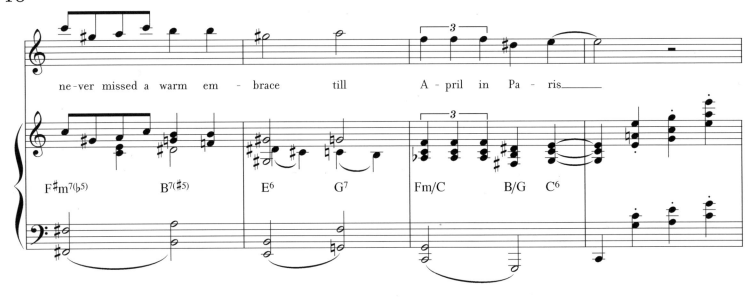

ne-ver missed a warm em - brace   till   A - pril in Pa - ris____

F#m⁷(♭5)   B⁷(♯5)   E⁶   G⁷   Fm/C   B/G   C⁶

Whom can I run to?____   What have you done to____   my

Em⁷(♭5)   Am¹³(maj⁷)   A¹³   D¹³   C   G⁷

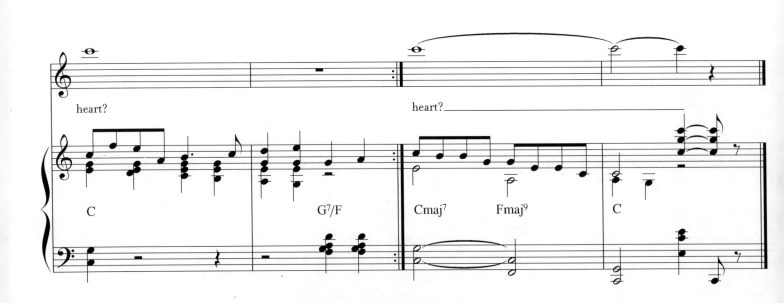

heart?   heart?____

C   G⁷/F   Cmaj⁷   Fmaj⁹   C

As Time Goes By

Words and Music by Herman Hupfeld

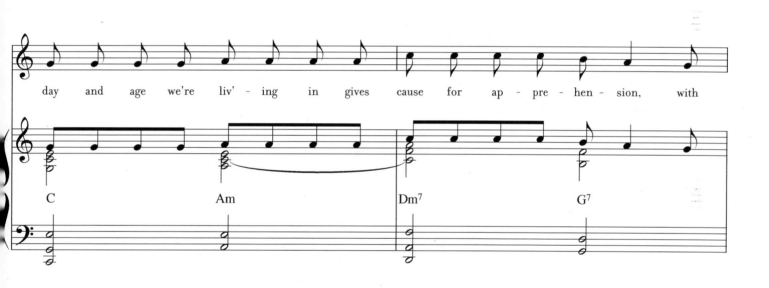

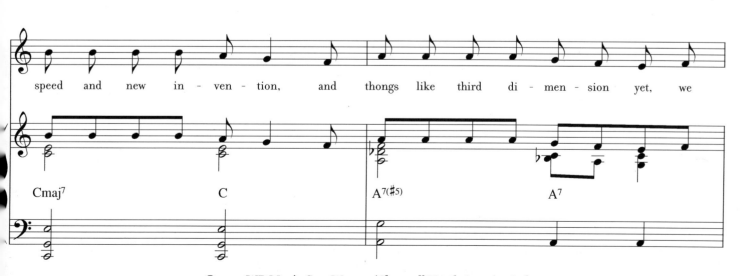

Autumn In New York

Words and Music by Vernon Duke

Moderately

B♭maj7　A♭maj7　G♭maj7　E♭maj7　D♭maj7　A♭maj7　Gm7(♭5)　C7

It's time to end my lone-ly ho-li-day,___ and bid the coun-try a has-ty fare-well.

B♭/F　C7　F/A　F/C　C7　Fm　C

So on this grey and mel-an-cho-ly day, I'll move to a Man-hat-tan ho-tel. I'll dis-

B♭/F　C7　F/A　Bdim7　A♭/E♭　E♭maj7(♯5)　A♭/E♭

Bewitched

Words by Lorenz Hart

Music by Richard Rodgers

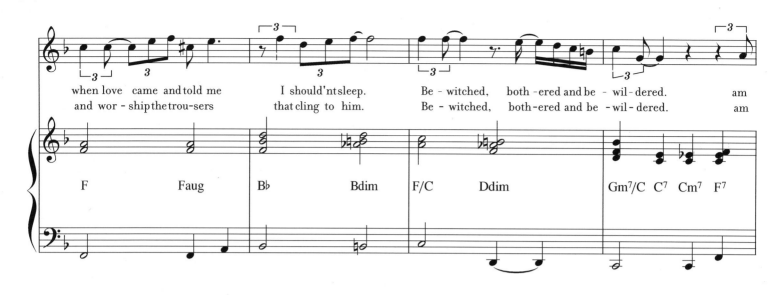

when love came and told me / I should'nt sleep. / Be-witched, both-ered and be-wil-dered. am
and wor-ship the trou-sers / that cling to him. / Be-witched, both-ered and be-wil-dered. am

F   Faug   Bb   Bdim   F/C   Ddim   Gm7/C C7 Cm7 F7

I._____ / Lost my heart, but what of it. He is
I._____ / When he talks he is seek-ing words to

Bbmaj7   Am7   D   Gm   Gm(maj7)   Gm7   Gm6

cold___ I a-gree. / He can laugh, but I love it,___ al-though the
get___ off his chest. / Ho-ri zontal-ly___ he's at his

Dm   Dm(maj7)   Dm7   Dm6   Bbmaj7   Am7   Gm7   Gm7/C   C7

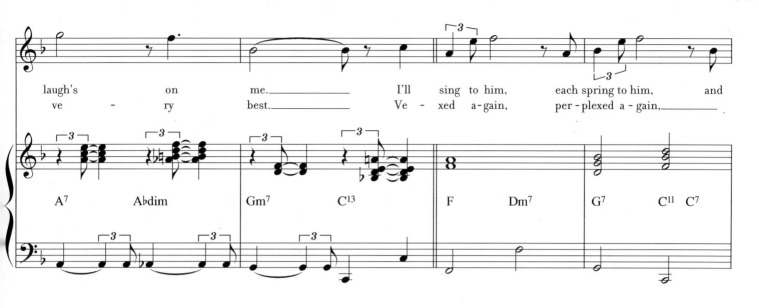

laugh's on me._____ I'll sing to him, each spring to him, and
ve - ry best._____ Ve - xed a - gain, per - plexed a - gain,_____

A⁷ A♭dim Gm⁷ C¹³ F Dm⁷ G⁷ C¹¹ C⁷

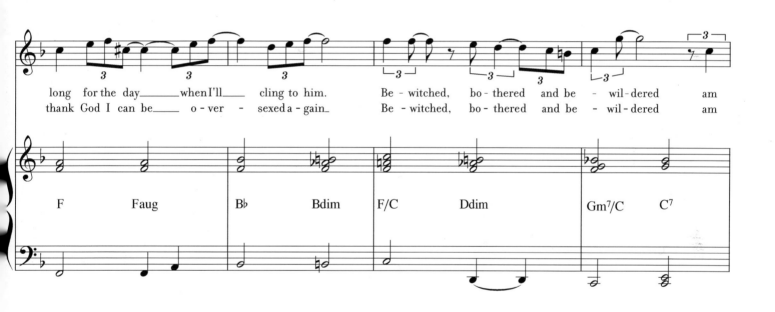

long for the day_____ when I'll_____ cling to him. Be - witched, bo - thered and be - wil - dered am
thank God I can be_____ o - ver - sexed a - gain_ Be - witched, bo - thered and be - wil - dered am

F Faug B♭ Bdim F/C Ddim Gm⁷/C C⁷

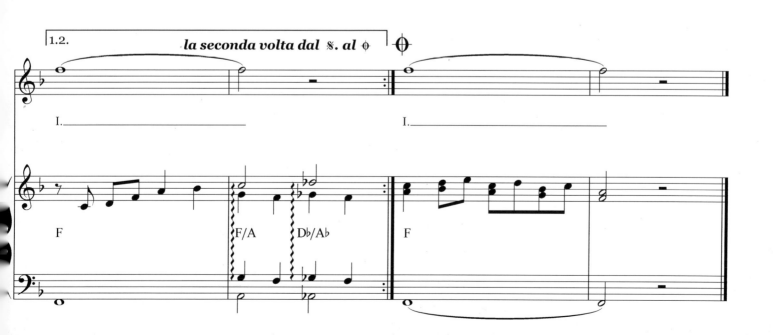

1.2. *la seconda volta dal ℅. al ⌀*

I._____ I._____

F F/A D♭/A♭ F

But Not For Me

from Girl Crazy

Music and Lyrics by George Gershwin and Ira Gershwin

Old Man Sun-shine lis-ten, you! Nev-er tell me, "Dreams come true!" Just try it And I'll start a ri-ot. Bea-trice Fair-fax, don't you dare Ev-er tell me he will care; I'm

Do, Do, Do

from Oh, Kay!

Music and Lyrics by George Gershwin and Ira Gershwin

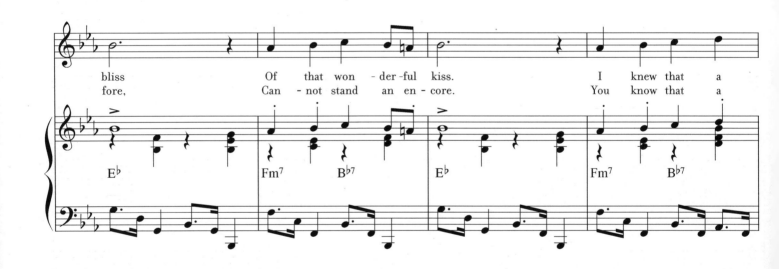

Dream A Little Dream Of Me

Words by Gus Kahn

Music by Fabian Andre and Wilbur Schwandts

Moderately, with swing

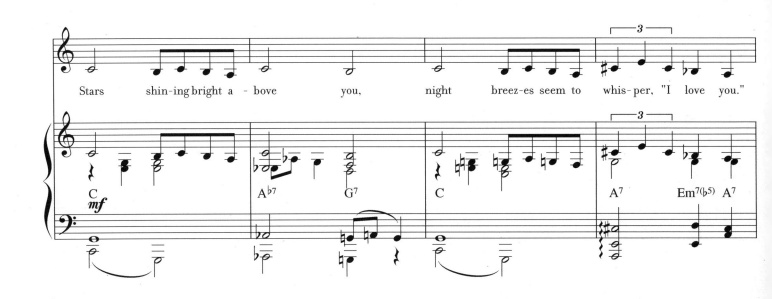

Stars shin-ing bright a - bove you, night breez-es seem to whis-per, "I love you."

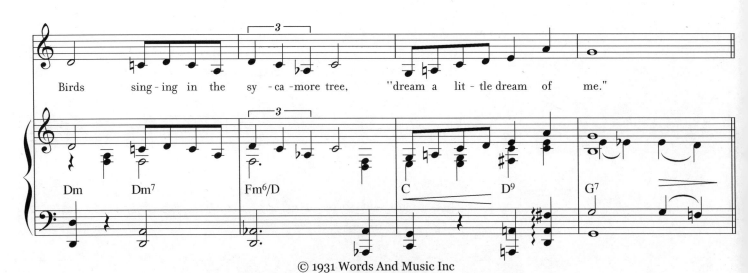

Birds sing-ing in the sy - ca-more tree, "dream a lit - tle dream of me."

Embraceable You

from Girl Crazy

Music and Lyrics by George Gershwin and Ira Gershwin

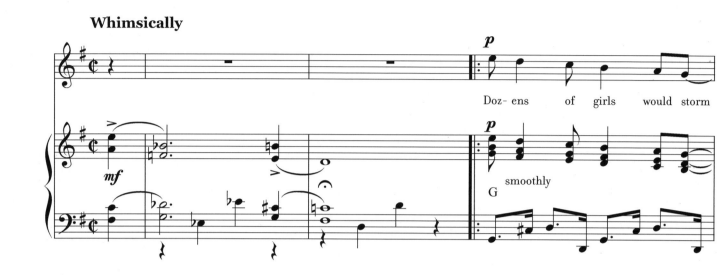

46

Ev'ry Time We Say Goodbye

Words and Music by Cole Porter

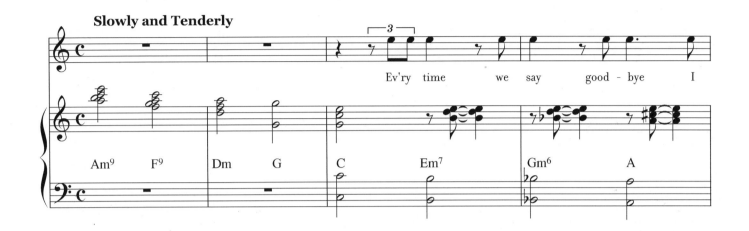

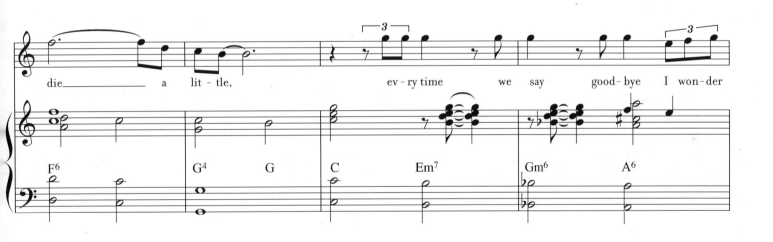

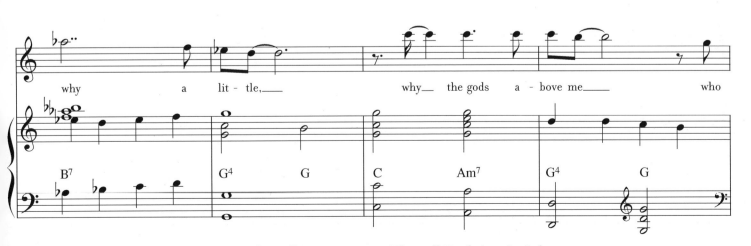

strange the change_____ from ma - jor to mi - nor_____ ev - ry time

A⁷ F Fm⁶ Fm E♭ Fm⁶ C⁴ Am⁷

fisarmomica

we say good - bye._____

F⁶ G C Am F

G⁴ G C Cmaj⁷ C Fm⁷

G⁴ G C Em⁷ Gm⁶ A⁷ F⁶

Fascinating Rhythm

from Lady, Be Good

Music and Lyrics by George Gershwin and Ira Gershwin

I Get A Kick Out Of You

Words and Music by Cole Porter

Bright swing

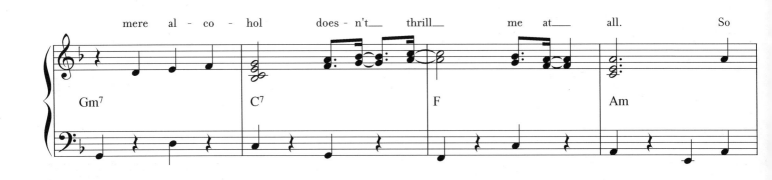

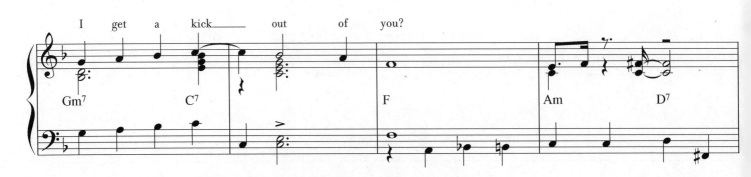

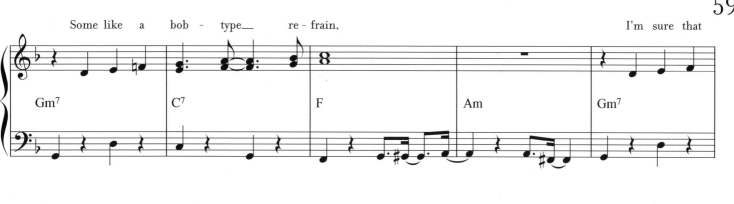

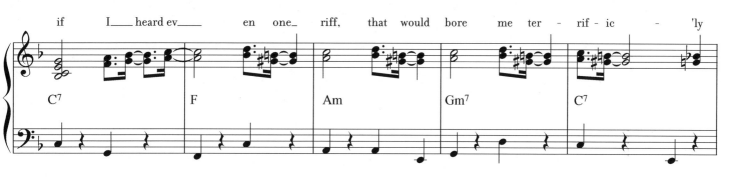

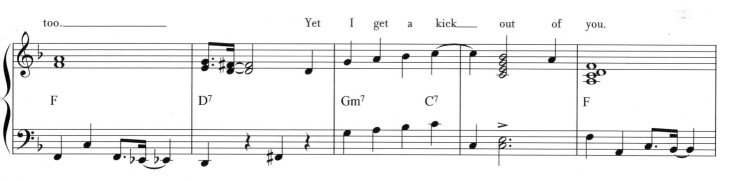

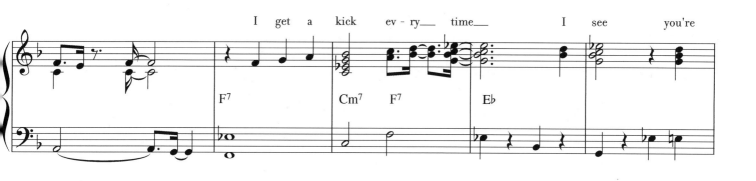

I Got Rhythm

from Girl Crazy

Music and Lyrics by George Gershwin and Ira Gershwin

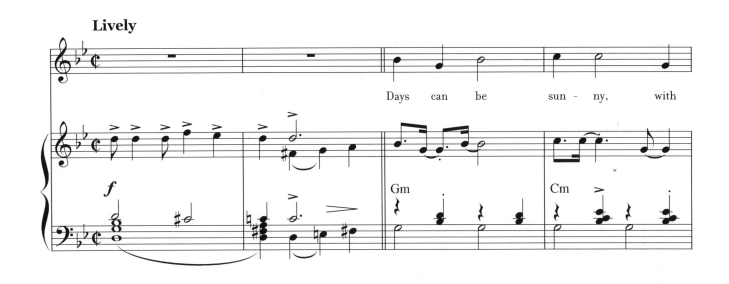

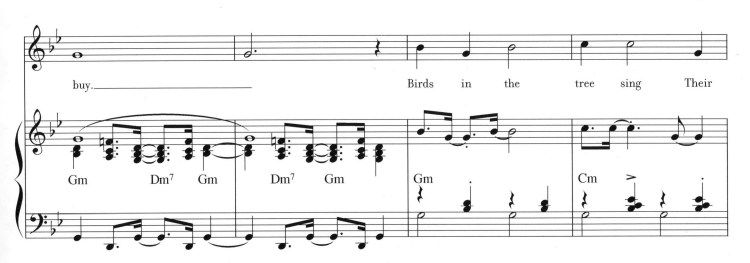

I Hear A Rhapsody

Words and Music by George Fragos, Jack Baker and Dick Gasparre

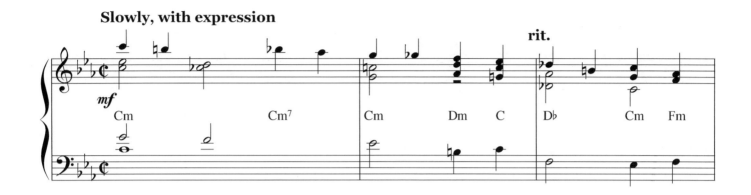

I'll Build A Stairway To Paradise

from George White's Scandals Of 1922

Words by Buddy De Sylva and Ira Gershwin

Music by George Gershwin

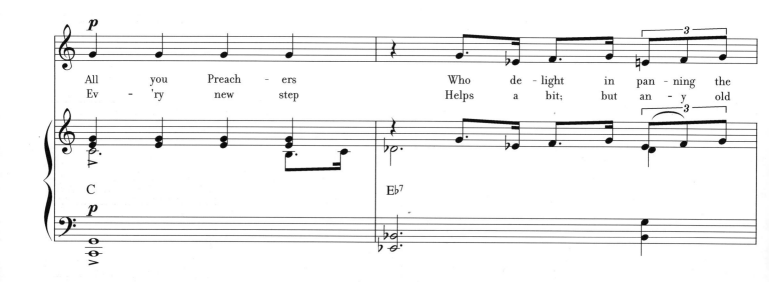

All you Preach - ers Who de - light in pan - ning the
Ev - 'ry new step Helps a bit; but an - y old

dan - cing teach - ers, Let me tell you there are a lot of fea - tures
kind of two - step Does as well. It don't mat - ter what step you step,

It Ain't Necessarily So

from Porgy And Bess

Music and Lyrics by George Gershwin, Du Bose and Dorothy Heyward and Ira Gershwin

It Had To Be You

Words by Gus Kahn

Music by Isham Jones

It's Only A Paper Moon

Words by E. Y. Harburg and Billy Rose

Music by Harold Arlen

Moderately

poco rall.

G *f* G#dim7   Am7   D7 D#dim7   Em   A9   D11   D7

a tempo rubato

I ne-ver feel a thing is real when I'm a -way-from you, out of your em-

Am   G   Am   G   Am   G D9 G   Am7   D7

-brace, the world's a tem-po-ra-ry park-ing place,

G   Am   D7   G

  mm   mm   mm   mm, a bub - ble

C   G/B   Am7   D7   G   Gdim7/A#

Yes, it's on-ly a can-vas sky

G♯dim⁷ Am⁷ D⁷

G

hang - ing o- ver a mus -lin tree,___ but it would- n't be

Am⁷ D⁹ G G/B Bm⁷(♭⁵)

make be - lieve,___ if you be -lieved in me.___ With

C⁶ D⁷ G

out your love, it's a hon - ky -tonk pa - rade, with-

C⁶ Cm⁷ Gmaj⁷ D¹¹ Am⁹ D⁹ G

I've Got a Crush On You

from Strike Up The Band

Music and Lyrics by George Gershwin and Ira Gershwin

I've Got You Under My Skin

Words and Music by Cole Porter

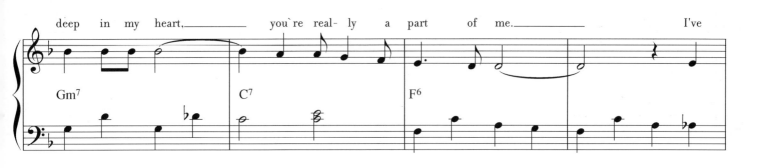

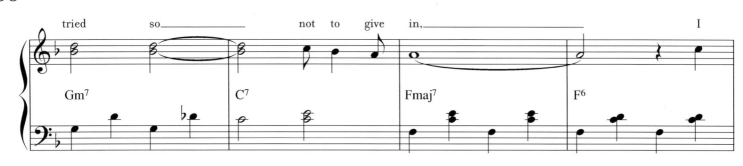

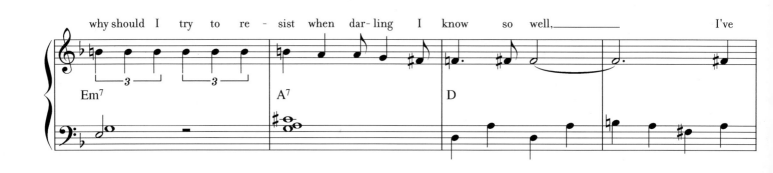

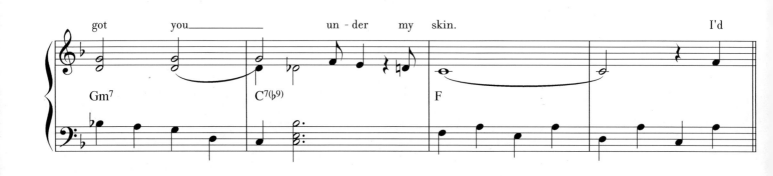

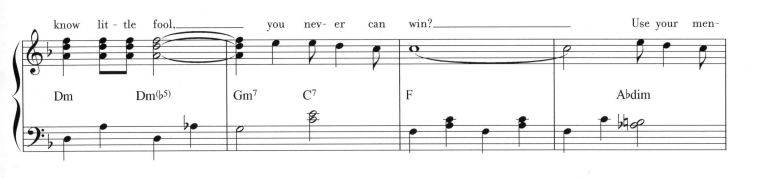

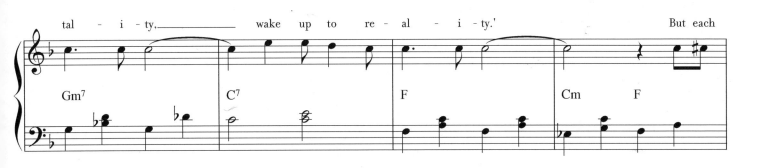

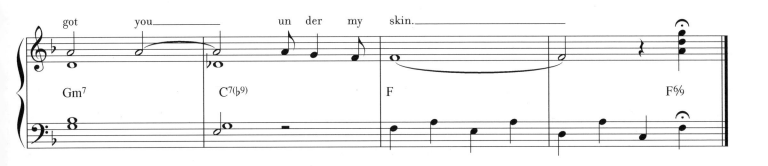

Let There Be Love

Words by Ian Grant

Music by Lionel Rand

Medium swing tempo

Liza
(All The Clouds'll 'Roll Away)

Words by Ira Gershwin, George Gershwin and Gus Kahn

Music by Ira Gershwin and George Gershwin

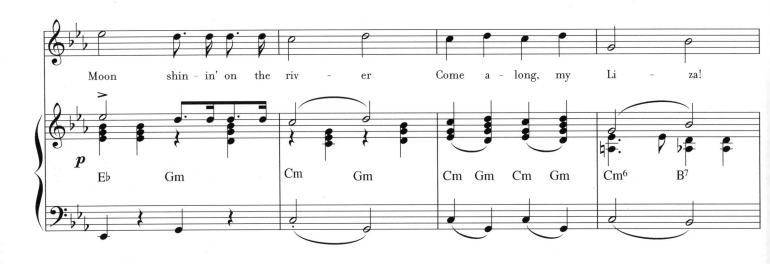

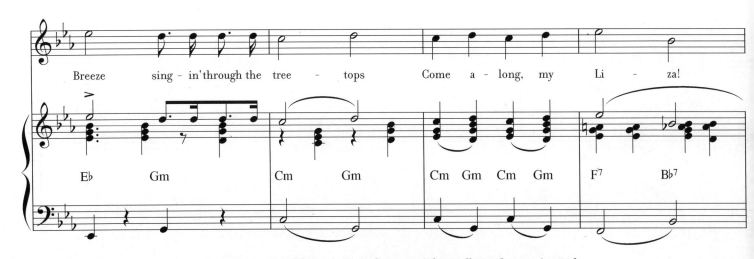

My Baby Just Cares For Me

Words by Gus Kahn

Music by Walter Donaldson

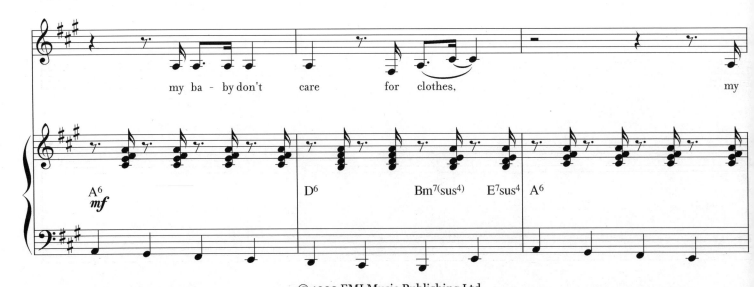

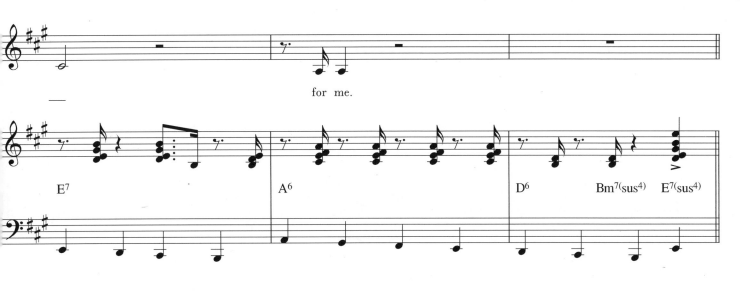

for me.

E⁷ A⁶ D⁶ Bm⁷⁽ˢᵘˢ⁴⁾ E⁷⁽ˢᵘˢ⁴⁾

PIANO SOLO with Basso

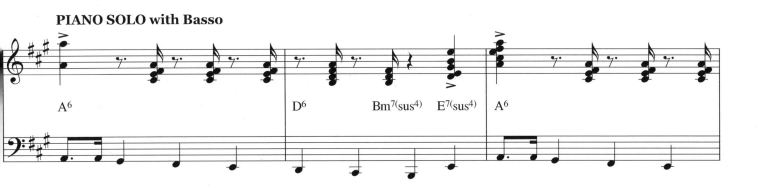

A⁶ D⁶ Bm⁷⁽ˢᵘˢ⁴⁾ E⁷⁽ˢᵘˢ⁴⁾ A⁶

D⁶ Bm⁷⁽ˢᵘˢ⁴⁾ E⁷⁽ˢᵘˢ⁴⁾ A

Basso pizz.

Bm⁷ E⁹ C♯⁷

Night And Day

Words and Music by Cole Porter

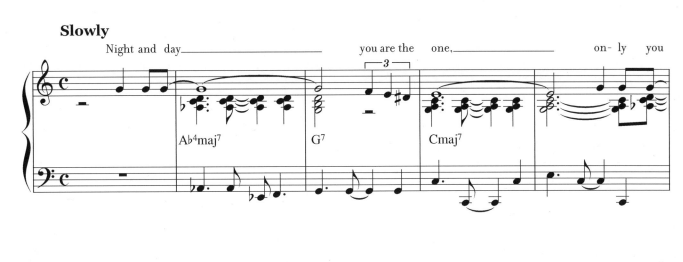

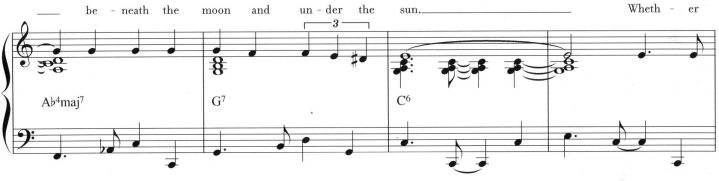

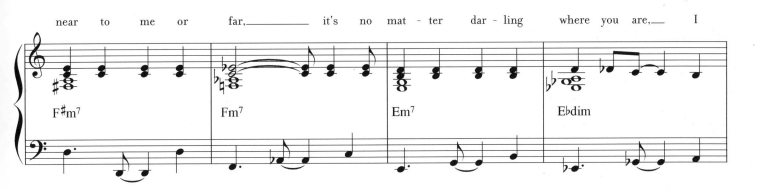

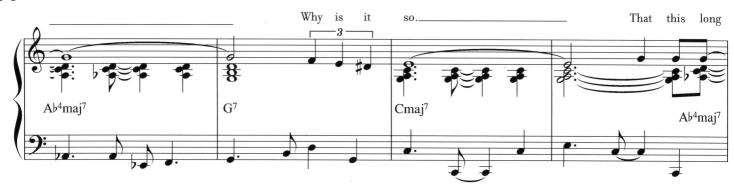

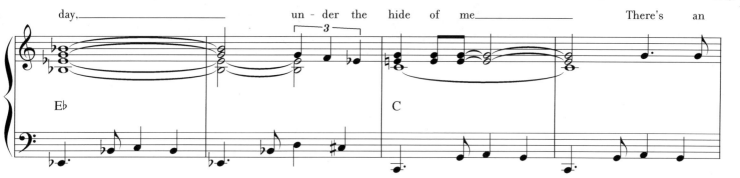

day,_____ un - der the hide of me_____ There's an

Eb   C

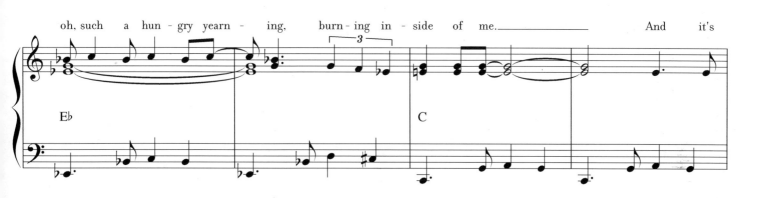

oh, such a hun - gry yearn - ing, burn - ing in - side of me._____ And it's

Eb   C

tor - ment won't be through_____ un - til you let spend my life ma - king love__ to you,

F#m⁷   Fm⁷   Em⁷   Ebdim

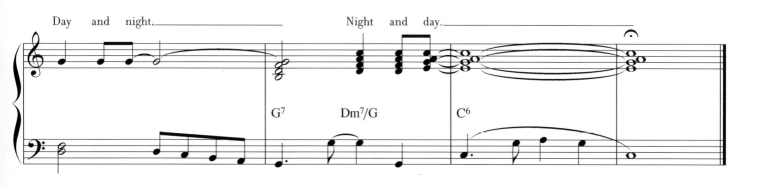

Day and night,_____ Night and day._____

G⁷   Dm⁷/G   C⁶

On The Sunny Side Of The Street

Words and Music by Dorothy Fields and Jimmy McHugh

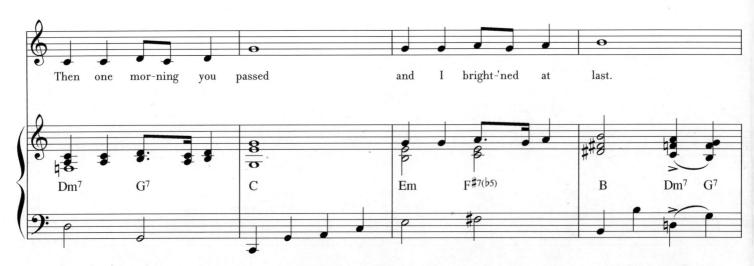

113

'Round Midnight

Words and Music by Cootie Williams, Bernie Hanighen and Thelonius Monk

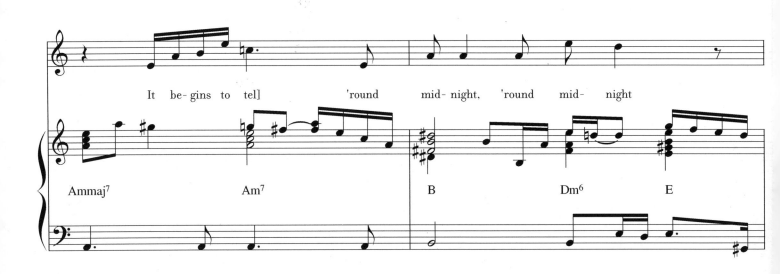

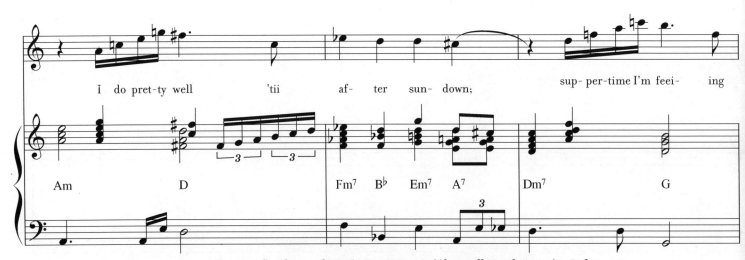

'S Wonderful

from Funny Face

Music and Lyrics by George Gershwin and Ira Gershwin

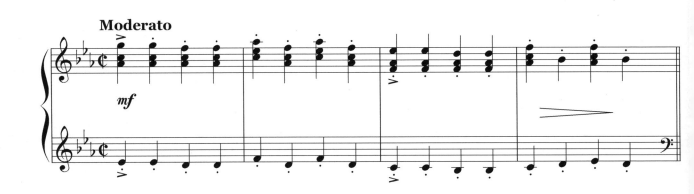

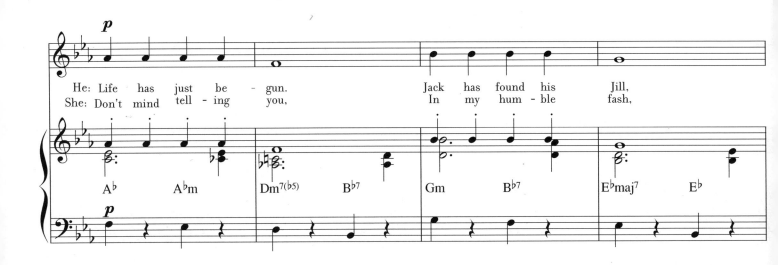

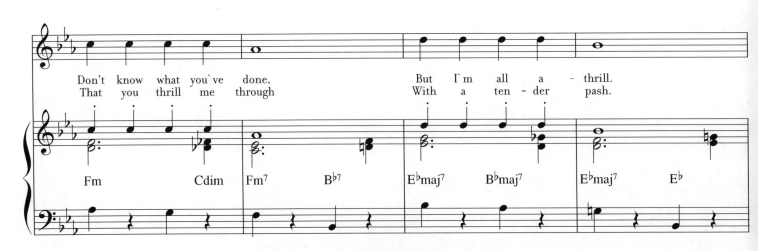

Somebody Loves Me

from George White's Scandals Of 1924

Words by Buddy De Sylva and Ballard MacDonald

Music by George Gershwin

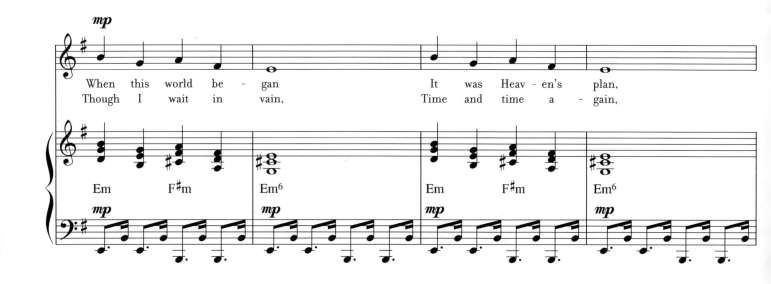

When this world be - gan, It was Heav - en's plan,
Though I wait in vain, Time and time a - gain,

There should be a girl for ev - 'ry sin - gle man;
No one ev - er meets me down in Lov - er's Lane.

SOON

Music and Lyrics by George Gershwin and Ira Gershwin

Moderately

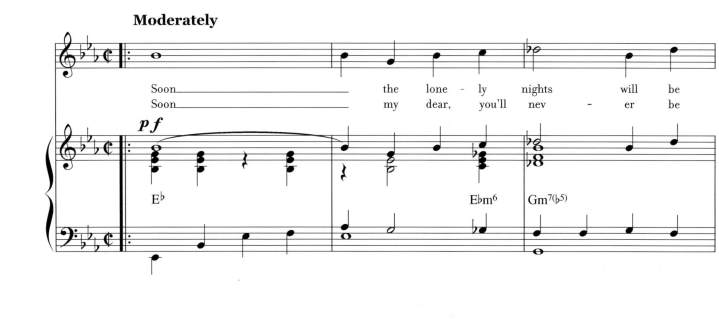

Soon_____ the lone - ly nights will be
Soon_____ my dear, you'll nev - er be

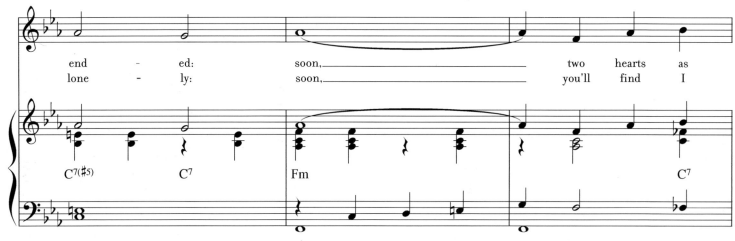

end - ed: soon,_____ two hearts as
lone - ly: soon,_____ you'll find I

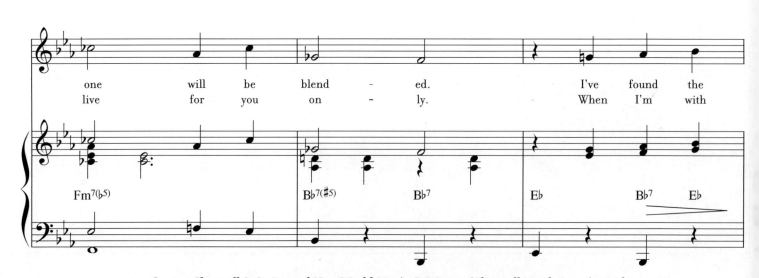

one will be blend - ed. I've found the
live for you on - ly. When I'm with

Stormy Weather

Words by Ted Koehler

Music by Harold Arlen

Slow lament, slightly swing

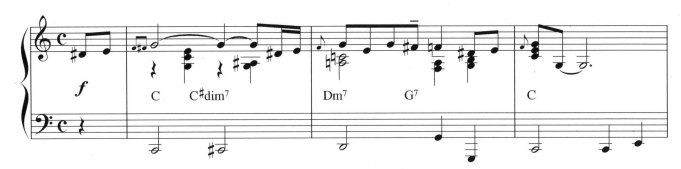

Summertime

from Porgy And Bess

Words and Music by George Gershwin, Dubose Heyward, Dorothy Heyward and Ira Gershwin

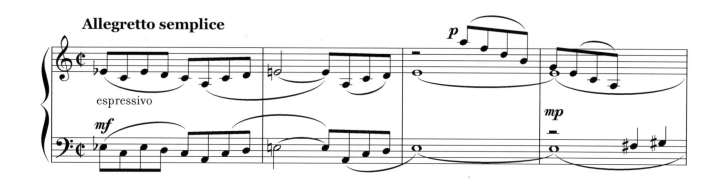

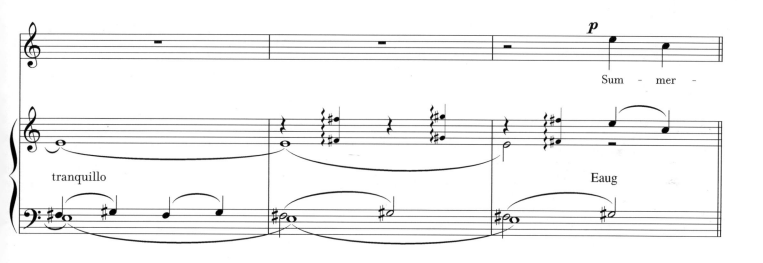

Swanee
from Capitol Revue

Words by Irving Caesar

Music by George Gershwin

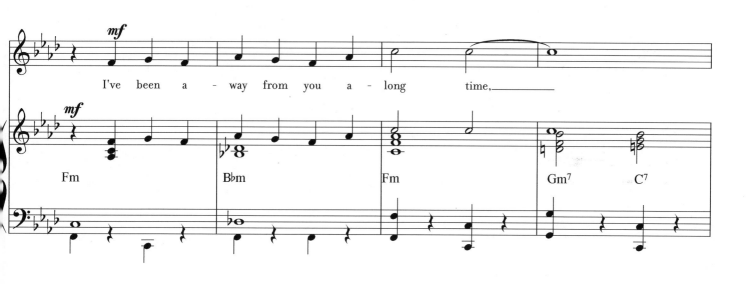

I've been a - way from you a - long time,____

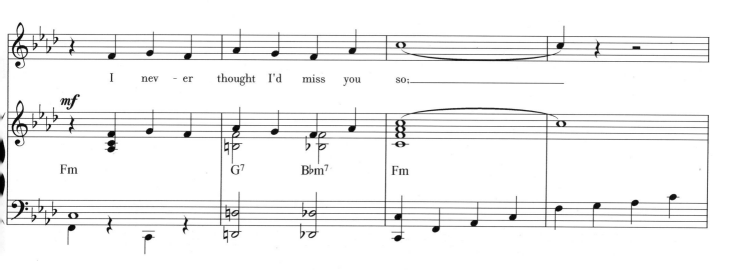

I nev - er thought I'd miss you so;____

The Lady Is A Tramp

Words by Lorenz Hart

Music by Richard Rodgers

The Man I Love

from Lady, Be Good

Music and Lyrics by George Gershwin and Ira Gershwin

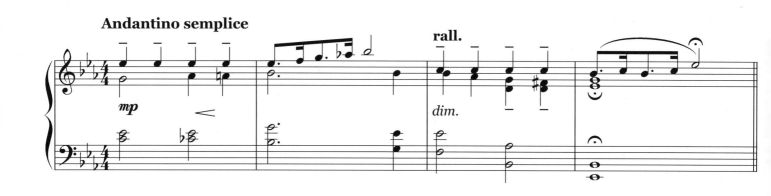

Thriving From A Riff

Music by Charlie Parker

When I Fall In Love

Words by Edward Heyman

Music by Victor Young

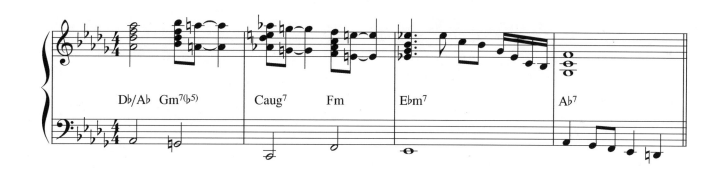

When I fall in love, it will be for-ev-er,

or I'll ne-ver fall in love. In a

You Go To My Head

Words by Haven Gillespie

Music by Fred J. Coots

Who Wants To Be A Millionaire

Words and Music by Cole Porter

Lively foxtrot